COOK YOURSELF SLIM

Created by Calorie Watchers Ltd

Recipes by Hari Krishna Pokhrel
Chef at *Truc Vert*, Mayfair, London

COOK yourself SLIM

Copyright © 2014 Calorie Watchers Ltd

First published in UK 2014 by Calorie Watchers Ltd

Author & Publisher : Calorie Watchers Ltd
Photography: Subhash Singh and Natalie Singh
Editor: Calorie Watchers Ltd
Recipes: Hari Pokrel
Styling: Subhash Singh, Natalie Singh and Hari Pokrel
Graphic Design: Artistic Visions – www.artisticvisions.co.uk

ISBN: 978-0-9929392-0-5

This book is only intended to provide general information and is not intended to replace any medical advice given by your health care professional. Calorie Watchers Ltd will not be liable for any damages or claims. We recommend you consult your physician before deciding to change your diet.

COOK yourself SLIM recipes features Eat Water® – Slim Noodles®, Slim Rice® and Slim Pasta® products, available in UK, Europe and USA.

Nutritional information may vary slightly if using different food brands.

Contents

Smoothie Recipes

Soup Recipes

Pasta Recipes

Noodles Recipes

Rice Recipes

Preface

Calorie Watchers Ltd is a UK based company owned by a healthcare professional, keen gym goer, a mother and a passionate cook who is proud to announce the launch of her first cookbook with a twist: *COOK yourself SLIM*.

COOK yourself SLIM explores a diverse range of recipes that are easy and stress-free to make. Most importantly these recipes are low in calories but do not compromise on the taste and portion sizes as you would expect with diet meals.

Calorie Watchers Ltd is about simplifying the whole area of weight loss, integrating balanced calorie reduced meals and simple exercises, getting us to make real positive changes.

Calorie Watchers Ltd, Eat Water® (the company that has brought us the Slim Pasta®, Slim Noodles® and Slim Rice®) and Hari Pokrel (chef at Truc Vert Restaurant, Mayfair, London) have brought together the different pieces necessary to smooth the transition to an effective and healthy weight loss regime.

Calorie Watchers Ltd has incorporated the Eat Water® range of products in their cookbook as it is a low calorie and low carb, pasta, noodles and rice range made from Konjac (an Asian root vegetable).

Hari Krishna Pokhrel
Chef at Truc Vert, Mayfair, London

"2.8 million people die each year as a result of diet-related chronic diseases" - WHO

I'm a chef who loves to make food. I am not from a background of physicians or scientists nor do I have access to research facilities to do tests and give you empirical data. Yet, I do have one story to share with you.

My brother is a type-2 diabetic, and as a result of his long struggle with weight management and improper diet, doctors have advised him to lose 3st (20kg) or he will in time develop some serious heart complications amongst other medical issues related to being over-weight.

I remember the concern on his face on hearing what the doctors advised and decided to help him with simple recipes that may improve his eating habits. Being diabetic and overweight left very little choices for him, so I searched the net and to my surprise found Slim Pasta®, Slim Noodles® and Slim Rice® that has no carbs. This was just the perfect product for an overweight diabetic.

When for the first time I received Slim Pasta®, I wasn't sure how they would taste, so I tried a few strands of spaghetti, it tasted like water – not a bad start! Using a few ingredients here and there I made a simple spaghetti bolognese. It tasted just like the real meal. That's when my brother and I fell in love (and no spike in his blood sugar too) with the Slim Pasta® range.

My brother has lost 2 stones in as many months using Slim range products and now he is very happy enjoying his low carb balanced meals. He is feeling a lot healthier, lighter, and his diabetes has also reduced.

I would recommend anyone trying to lose weight to have the Slim Pasta, noodle, rice range.

I am honoured Calorie Watchers accepted my culinary skills to create recipes for all to enjoy and help those who are really struggling to lose weight.

Planning and setting a goal

On behalf of Calorie Watchers Ltd, we congratulate you on taking this important step to improve your health.

As with any important task, planning is very important. This is a huge step in your life to lose weight and keep the weight off, therefore it is important to set steps and tick the boxes as we go along.

Step 1: It is important to get a clearance from your GP before starting any new meal plan and exercise program.

Step 2: Set your goal. (be realistic - smalls changes will magnify in the long term)

Step 3: Be positive and make changes to your food shopping habits, reorganize your fridge and your food storage cupboard. You know you are worth all this effort.

Step 4: Remember, water is better than fruit juices and alcohol. You don't need to take any extra calories. Try to do a 5 to 6 week alcohol detox and see how you feel. Drink 8 to 10 glasses of water daily.

TIPS:

Don't weigh yourself everyday, instead note your weight once a week. In the first few weeks you may not see a change in your weight, or it may even go up. Don't be alarmed. This could mean you have reduced body fat and built muscle (muscle weighs more than fat).

As an indication of fat loss, try on a piece of clothing... a blouse, jeans or trousers that were a little tight before you started the exercise and meal plan. A few weeks into your new regime, it should fit comfortably even though your weight may not have dropped (now you are smiling!).

Believe in yourself. There are no secrets. Follow your commitment. Find a supporting companion (in the gym, work place, or at home) who can support you on those dull days. Or contact Calorie Watchers Ltd for that important motivational support.

Remember it is the small changes in our lives that are magnified ten fold to give us the desired pleasures of happiness.

Ready, Steady, GO

Now that you have planned and set a goal, lets not wait any longer.

Print the appropriate 7 day Calorie Watchers meal plan from *www.EatWater. co.uk* as per your set goal.

We have devised the meal plans on the basis of weight control, 1 lb a week weight loss guide and 2 lbs a week weight loss guide. Any more lbs lost per week for a long period of time is not safe.

These meal plans are specifically designed keeping you in mind. These are not portion controlled as you would normally expect with diet plans and diet meals. What we have done by using the Eat Water® products is to give you the normal sized meal that will satisfy you and keep you full for longer as these products contain Konjac (a vegetable fibre that holds a lot more water than any other fibre). This means your stomach emptying rate is much more slower than using a regular or diet meals. Another advantage of using Eat Water® products is that we don't need to compromise on the taste by reducing the necessary fat that is required by your body. Remember Eat Water® Slim range products are carbohydrate-free, fat-free and almost calorie-free. Therefore, you are dieting without really trying!

Use the meal plan as a guide and follow the exercise plan as per your 7 day guide and you are on your way to a new you.

Exercises

Most of us know by now that we should be exercising on a regular basis. Not only does working out help you shed a few pounds, but there are also many other compelling reasons to include some regular activity in your routine.

Have you ever heard the expression "use it or lose it"? It's true! If you don't use your body, you will surely lose it. Your muscles will become flabby and weak. Your heart and lungs won't function efficiently. And your joints will be stiff and easily injured. Inactivity is as much of a health risk as smoking!

Here we have listed some very basic exercises you can do at home without any equipment. All you need to do is 3 to 4 sets of 10 or 12 reps. Total workout time of just 20 minutes. Make sure you warm up before doing exercises.

Jog on the Spot

Literally jog on the spot.

Skipping

Literally skip.

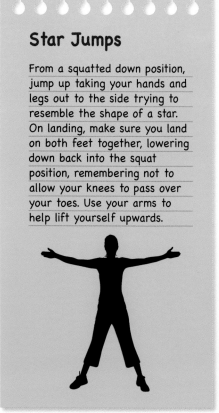

Star Jumps

From a squatted down position, jump up taking your hands and legs out to the side trying to resemble the shape of a star. On landing, make sure you land on both feet together, lowering down back into the squat position, remembering not to allow your knees to pass over your toes. Use your arms to help lift yourself upwards.

Burpees

Begin in a standing position. Drop into a squat position with your hands on the ground. Kick your feet back, while keeping your arms extended. Immediately return your feet to the squat position. Stand up from the squat position.

Superman Back Extension

Lay on your stomach and reach your arms forward (like you're flying). Gently raise your legs and upper body off the floor while keeping your head straight. Pause for three seconds and repeat.

Walking Lunge

Stand with feet shoulder-width apart and place your arms to the side. Step forward with your right foot and lower your left knee towards the floor. Your knees should bend about 90 degrees. Ensure your right knee stays over your right ankle and don't let your knee go past your toes. Step up to balance on your right foot and switch feet.

Squats

Stand tall with your feet shoulder-width apart and lower your hips (almost like you're sitting in a chair). As you bend your knees, your thighs will be parallel with the floor, Ensure your knees don't go beyond your toes and keep your chest up and look straight ahead. Stand back up to start position and repeat.

Skaters/Leaps

To start, get into a semi-squat position and leap sideways to land on your right foot. Immediately push off in the opposite direction and land on your left foot. Make sure you perform these skaters continuously.

Single Leg Balance Stick

Balance on your right foot with your left foot behind you. Lean forward, keeping a straight body position and lift your left heel towards the ceiling. Maintain a slight bend in your standing knee so you don't lock your knee. If you're having trouble balancing, focus on something in front of you or hold your back leg for initial support (pictured here).

Side Plank Hip Drops

Begin by lying on your right side with your right elbow directly lined under your shoulder. Keeping your feet on the floor, lift your hips off the floor and support your body with your forearm. Hold for three seconds and slowly lower your right hip onto the floor and repeat.

Stair Climbing

Literally run up the stairs and walk down.

Triceps Push Ups

Place your hands on the floor and keep them under your shoulders. Holding your body straight, bend your elbows close to your body. Lower your chest between your hands and push back up into the starting position. If you're having trouble completing a push-up, place your knees on the floor to make things easier. For intensity, raise your feet up onto stairs or an elevated surface to increase the difficulty.

Bird Dog

Begin on all fours (downward dog), ensuring your hands are directly under your shoulders and your knees are directly under your hips. Slowly extend your right leg behind you and reach your right arm forward into a straight line. Hold your balance without arching your back. Return to the starting position and repeat on the opposite side.

Plank Crawl

Pace yourself for this one. We recommend giving yourself a goal of 15 to 20 crawls. Begin this move in a push-up position with your elbows close to your body. Lower yourself down one arm at a time into a plank position on your forearms, while keeping your elbows directly under your shoulders. Push back up one arm at a time into your starting push-up position. Alternate the arm you lead with and maintain a straight body throughout the movement. Lower your knees to the floor to decrease the difficulty level.

Bridge

Lay on your back with your arms by your sides. Bend your knees while keeping your feet flat on the floor. Maintaining a straight back, raise your hips up to a straight line from your shoulders to your knees. Hold for three seconds and lower your hips slowly back to the floor and repeat.

Diet Myths

Will crash dieting or fasting help lose weight?

Yes in short term you will lose weight, but ultimately it can hinder weight loss. Fasting can make you weak. Losing weight over long term burns fat. Crash dieting or fasting not only removes fat but also lean muscle and tissue. The loss of lean muscle causes a fall in your basal metabolic rate (BMR) – see page 11. This means your body will need fewer calories than it did previously, making weight gain more likely once you stop dieting. This is the reason why exercise is recommended with any weight-loss plan to build muscle and maintain your metabolic rate.

Are low-fat or no-fat diets good for you?

There's no need to follow a fat-free diet. Our bodies need fat for energy, tissue repair and to transport vitamins A, D, E and K around the body. Cutting down on saturated fats and eating unsaturated fats, found in fish, nuts, olive oil and avocados, will help.

Does slow metabolism prevent weight loss?

This is a common myth among dieters who struggle to lose weight. Studies have shown that the resting metabolism increased as people become fatter. Therefore, larger you are, the more calories you need to keep your body going and the higher your metabolism.

Weight gain occurs when the number of calories eaten is greater than the number of calories used up by the body.

Calorie Calculator

This Calorie Calculator is based on the Mifflin St Jeor equation. With this equation, the Basal Metabolic Rate (BMR) is calculated by using the following formula:

BMR = 10 X weight(kg) + 6.25 X height(cm) – 5 X age(y) +5   (man)
BMR = 10 X weight(kg) + 6.25 X height(cm) – 5 X age(y) +161   (woman)

The calories needed to maintain your weight equal to BMR value, multiplied by an activity factor. To lose 1 lb (0.5kg) per week, you will need to shave 500 calories from your daily meals.

The best way to lose weight is through proper diet and exercise. Try not to lower your calorie intake by more than 1000 calories per day, and try to lower your calorie intake gradually.

To maintain your weight you need 2207 calories per day.

Weight Loss:

To lose 2 lb (1kg) a week, you need 1207 calories per day.

Weight Gain:

To gain 2 lb (1 kg) a week, you need 3207 calories per day.

Key:

Wheat Free

Gluten Free

Dairy Free

7 Day Meal

	Breakfast	Snack	Lunch	Snack
Monday	Green tea Morning power smoothie pg. 32	Fruit	Chicken laksa soup pg. 70	Roasted almonds (25g)
	405 kcal	75 kcal	240 kcal	160 kcal
Tuesday	Fruit tea Pinocado smoothie pg. 36	Apple	Gazpacho soup pg. 68	Mixed nuts (30g)
	278 kcal	70 kcal	317 kcal	158 kcal
Wednesday	Lemon and warm water drink 50 Second smoothie pg. 20	Fruit	Beef and noodle soup pg. 72	Fruit yogurt
	287 kcal	75 kcal	302 kcal	122 kcal
Thursday	Mint tea Warrior smoothie pg. 40	Banana	Hot and sour soup pg. 54	Roasted almonds (25g)
	266 kcal	155 kcal	144 kcal	160 kcal
Friday	Green tea Blueberry Tofu smoothie pg. 22	Fruit yogurt	Chicken noodle soup pg. 52	Mixed nuts (30g)
	277 kcal	122 kcal	225 kcal	158 kcal
Saturday	Lemon and warm water drink Naughty smoothie pg. 34	Apple	Italian meatballs soup pg. 64	Fruit salad
	361 kcal	70 kcal	224 kcal	75 kcal
Sunday	Fruit tea Green Cherry Berry smoothie pg. 28	Roasted almonds (25g)	Wanton noodle soup pg. 56	Wholewheat cracker and soft cheese
	119 kcal	160 kcal	505 kcal	143 kcal

Dinner	Desert	Exercise	Calorie intake
Chicken stir-fry rice pg. 134	Mint tea after dinner is perfect for those who have a sweet tooth	see pg. 6–9 (don't forget to warm up first) Stair climbing - 3 sets Triceps push-ups - 3 sets Bridge - 3 sets	
444 kcal			1324 kcal
Yakisoba pg. 108	None	Star jumps - 3 sets Skipping - 10 mins Plank crawl - 3 sets	
467 kcal			1290 kcal
Alla carbonara pg. 78	None	Jog on the spot - 10 mins Single leg balance stick - 4 sets Walking lunges - 3 sets	
430 kcal			1216 kcal
Thai fish curry & rice pg. 136	None	Burpees - 3 sets Plank crawl - 4 sets Walking lunges - 3 sets	
349 kcal			1074 kcal
Prawn and chilli pasta pg. 98	Frozen yoghurt	Jog on the spot - 10 mins Side plank hip drops - 3 sets Bird dog - 4 sets	
420 kcal	80 kcal		1282 kcal
Authentic lasagne pg. 80	Fruit mouse	Skipping - 10 mins Bridge - 4 sets Superman back extension - 3 sets	
430 kcal	79 kcal		1239 kcal
Mie Goreng pg. 106	Light chocolate mousse	Star jumps - 3 sets Plank crawl - 3 sets	
353 kcal	80 kcal		1360 kcal

SMOOTHIES

Smoothies will have you feeling great all day!

Smoothies Help Keep You Hydrated

A smoothie for breakfast helps you get hydrated at the start of the day, something soda and coffee won't do. Since your body pulls water from many foods in order to stay hydrated, you won't have to drink water when you're sipping on a smoothie (especially a homemade one without sugar). Milk and yogurt are largely water, so if your smoothie is dairy-based, you'll quench your thirst. This is especially handy if you only have one cup holder in your car. In hot weather, add a few ice cubes to the blender for extra water.

Milk-Based Smoothies Provide Calcium

Smoothies made with dairy products as the bulk provide calcium for bone strength. Try whole milk, whole milk yogurt or kefir. The cultured milk products are good sources of probiotics and live cultures. 250ml of milk provide almost a third of your daily requirement of calcium. Choose whole milk products rather than skim for optimal nutrition. The health benefits are questionable at best, while whole milk contains the fat and vitamins needed to assimilate calcium and protein found in milk.

Smoothies Make a Healthy Breakfast on the Go

A homemade smoothie for your morning meal is an excellent, on-the-go breakfast choice. You can make it in minutes before you leave the house and sip it on your way to work, school or those hectic school drop offs. A nutritious smoothie packs more usable nutrition than most multivitamins.

Smoothies Keep you Full for Longer

Blending Slim Noodles or Slim Rice with any smoothie will provide that extra fibre to keep you full for even longer. Drinking a smoothie in the morning keeps you from indulging in empty carbohydrates in the form of donuts and removes the temptation of the drive through.

50 SECONDS SMOOTHIE

...OK so its actually a milkshake but hey do you really care? This smoo... milk... errrrrrm... moothie can be made so quickly that you can be out of bed and out of the door with breakfast and still in time for that important board meeting or coffee morning after school drop offs!

½ pack of Slim Noodles/ Rice

1 banana

6 to 7 strawberries

250ml whole milk

1. Prepare Slim Noodles/Rice as per package instructions (drained and rinsed).
2. Really? You need instructions?
3. Chop banana, add strawberries, milk and Slim Noodles to a blender and smooth away.
4. Enjoy the coffee morning!

Nutritional Information/Serving

Energy	Protein	Carbo-hydrate	Fat	Saturated Fat	Sodium	Fibre
287 kcal	12.0g	56.0g	5.2g	3.0g	0.4g	3.4g

BLUEBERRY TOFU SMOOTHIE

Serves 1 | Prep. time 1 minutes | Cook time 1 minutes

Blueberry-Tofu smoothie is a simple and delicious way to use soy in your drinks. Tofu works well as a thickener in smoothies.

½ pack (100g) Slim Noodles

1 cup (150g) blueberries, frozen or fresh

50g silken tofu

½ cup (125ml) pomegranate juice

6 ice cubes

1 tbsp honey

2 tbsp Chia seeds

1. Prepare Slim Noodles as per package instructions (drained and rinsed).
2. Combine all the ingredients in a blender, and blend until smooth.
3. Enjoy

Nutritional Information/Serving

			Energy	Protein	Carbo-hydrate	Fat	Saturated Fat	Sodium	Fibre
			287 kcal	12.0g	56.0g	5.2g	3.0g	0.4g	3.4g

COCOKIWI SMOOTHIE

A fabulous tropical smoothie with succulent kiwi and nutritious coconut milk

Ingredients	Method
1 pack (200g) Slim Noodles/Rice	1. Prepare Slim Noodles/Rice as per package instructions (drained and rinsed).
200ml coconut milk	2. Blend all the ingredients together until smooth and enjoy.
330ml tender coconut water (Coco togo)	
5 cm cucumber	
1 banana	
2 kiwis, peeled	
4 strawberries	
10 cherries, pitted	
6 ice cubes	

Nutritional Information/Serving

	Energy	Protein	Carbo-hydrate	Fat	Saturated Fat	Sodium	Fibre
	270 kcal	3.0g	43.0g	9.2g	8.0g	0.1g	7.1g

GLOWING GREEN SMOOTHIE

Rich in immune-boosting nutrients. Green drinks get their vibrant colour from chlorophyll, a nutrient-rich pigment found in all leafy vegetable such as spinach, kale, celery and lettuce, that cleans the body of harmful toxins, oxygenates the blood and helps boost energy levels.

½ pack (100g) Slim Rice

1 cup (250ml) of water

1 head romaine lettuce, chopped

½ head of large bunch spinach

3 stalks of celery

1 apple, cored and chopped

1 pear, cored and chopped

1 banana

Juice of ½ lemon

1. Prepare Slim Rice as per package instructions (drained and rinsed).
2. Place all the ingredients into a blender.
3. Blend until smooth.
4. Enjoy

Nutritional Information/Serving

Energy	Protein	Carbo-hydrate	Fat	Saturated Fat	Sodium	Fibre
360 kcal	19.6g	69.2g	2.5g	0.3g	6.55g	16.3g

GREEN CHERRY BERRY SMOOTHIE

Serves
1

Prep. time
1
minutes

Cook time
1
minutes

This green smoothie is one of the few that is actually not green and is a low calorie smoothie. It's hard to believe since this smoothie is packed with fruits and veggies.

Ingredients	Instructions
1 pack (200g) of Slim Rice/Noodles	1. Prepare Slim Rice as per package instructions (drained and rinsed).
10 frozen cherries, pitted	2. Put all ingredients in a blender in order: spinach, cherries, raspberries, water, rice/noodles.
25 frozen raspberries	
bunch of washed baby spinach	3. Blend until smooth and enjoy.
250ml water	

Nutritional Information/Serving

			Energy	Protein	Carbo-hydrate	Fat	Saturated Fat	Sodium	Fibre
WHEAT FREE	GLUTEN FREE	DIARY FREE	119 kcal	5.0g	17.0g	1.1g	0.1g	0.1g	12.0g

JUBAMBO SMOOTHIE

This smoothie takes it's inspiration from a friend's recipe which he makes to keep him fuelled and full of energy for his long days at work and time in the gym!

½ (100g) pack of Slim Noodles/Rice

1 tbsp peanut butter

1 banana

40g rolled oats/muesli

100ml frozen yoghurt

200ml whole milk

pinch of cinnamon

add water if too thick for your liking

1. Prepare Slim Noodles/Rice as per package instructions (drained and rinsed).
2. Add all the ingredients in a blender.
3. Blend until smooth.
4. Enjoy your day!

Nutritional Information/Serving

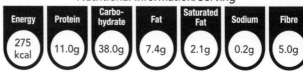

Energy	Protein	Carbo-hydrate	Fat	Saturated Fat	Sodium	Fibre
275 kcal	11.0g	38.0g	7.4g	2.1g	0.2g	5.0g

MORNING POWER SMOOTHIE

This hearty mix has cooked oatmeal and protein powder to fill you up and keep you satisfied until lunch. Oatmeal is a great source of complex carbohydrates that will give you the sustained energy you need to keep you going all morning.

2 banana

40g rolled oats

1 pack (200g) of Slim Rice/Noodles

2 (400ml) cups whole milk
(or non dairy alternative)

1 mango (if in season)

2 tbsp Chia seeds (optional)

pinch of ground nutmeg

*add water if too thick for your liking

1. Prepare Slim Rice/Noodles as per package instructions (drained and rinsed).
2. Place all the ingredients into a blender
3. Blend until smooth
4. Enjoy!

Nutritional Information/Serving

Energy	Protein	Carbo-hydrate	Fat	Saturated Fat	Sodium	Fibre
405 kcal	13.0g	65.0g	7.4g	7.9g	0.2g	10.7g

NAUGHTY SMOOTHIE

Naughty due to the chocolate, but nice to share with a loved one! A perfect smoothie for special days! Men - memorise this recipe to avoid the couch or dog-house. This is always a winner!!

100g of chocolate

1 pack (200g) of Slim Noodles/Rice

500ml whole milk

15 large strawberries

few leaves of mint

1. Prepare Slim Noodles/Rice as per package instructions (drained and rinsed).
2. Melt chocolate either in microwave or on the hob with half the milk.
3. When melted add the other half of milk (already warmed)
4. Add chocolate milk, Slim Noodles/Rice, strawberries and mint to smoothie maker.
5. Serve warm and enjoy.

Nutritional Information/Serving

Energy	Protein	Carbo-hydrate	Fat	Saturated Fat	Sodium	Fibre
361 kcal	13.0g	54.0g	16.2g	9.8g	0.4g	8.8g

PINOCADO SMOOTHIE

A perfect balance to a smoothie with avocado and pineapple. The silky rich and creamy taste to start the most perfect day!

1 pack (200g) of Slim Rice/Noodles

1 ripe avocado, seeded and peeled

1½ cup (200g) pineapple, roughly cut

1½ (350ml) cup orange juice

1 banana

1 tbsp honey

2 tsp lime juice

2 drops of vanilla extract

1 cup ice

1. Prepare Slim Rice/Noodles as per package instructions (drained and rinsed).
2. Combine all ingredients except ice in a blender.
3. Blend until smooth.
4. Add ice cubes and blend again. Enjoy immediately.

Nutritional Information/Serving

	Energy	Protein	Carbo-hydrate	Fat	Saturated Fat	Sodium	Fibre
	278 kcal	2.5g	44.0g	8.3g	1.8g	0.1g	7.0g

RENEWAL JUICE

This is an enzyme-rich green juice. Its great for providing energy, detoxifying and alkalizing your body.

½ pack (100g) Slim Noodles/Rice

330 ml tender coconut water (Coco togo)

1 bunch English spinach

1 handful mint

1 handful parsley

1 tbsp lemon juice

1 short cucumber, cut in half lengthways

A few lettuce leaves

4 celery stalks

1 floret broccoli

2 cm knob of fresh ginger, peeled

6 ice cubes

1. Prepare Slim Noodles/Rice as per package instructions (drained and rinsed).
2. Add all the ingredients in a blender except ice.
3. Pour into a glass and add ice cubes.
4. Enjoy!

Nutritional Information/Serving

Energy	Protein	Carbo-hydrate	Fat	Saturated Fat	Sodium	Fibre
163 kcal	9.0g	20.0g	2.0g	0.3g	0.39g	14.5g

WARRIOR SMOOTHIE

This smoothie has so many amazing benefits. It's like a nutritious meal in a glass - and it tastes super amazing.

1 pack (200g) Slim Noodles/Rice

3 stalks of kale (use leaves only)

½ head of romaine lettuce

1 banana

330ml tender coconut water (Coco togo)

handful of blueberries

2 tbsp chia seeds

30g hemp seeds

1 tbsp maca powder

1 tbsp spirulina

1. Prepare Slim Noodles/Rice as per package instructions (drained and rinsed).
2. Add all the ingredients in a blender.
3. Blend till smooth and enjoy.

Nutritional Information/Serving

Energy	Protein	Carbo-hydrate	Fat	Saturated Fat	Sodium	Fibre
266 kcal	11.0g	34.0g	9.4g	1.0g	0.1g	11.5g

BEEF STOCK

Makes
4
litres

Prep. time
15
minutes

Cook time
3
hours

Cooling
2–3
hours

This recipe makes a luscious stock, loaded with the delicious flavours of the roasted meat and vegetables.

Ingredients
1½ kg beef bones
10 spring fresh thyme
2 onions, halved or quartered
2 bay leaves
2 carrots, coarsely chopped
5 litres cold water
2 stalks celery, coarsely chopped
1 tsp whole black peppercorns
Small bunch fresh parsley

1. Preheat the oven to 200°C (gas 6). Place the beef bones, onions, carrots, and celery in a large roasting pan. Roast, stirring occasionally, for 1 ½ hours, until browned.

2. Tie the parsley, thyme, and bay leaves with kitchen string to make a bouquet garni.

3. Transfer the beef bones and vegetables into a large soup pot over medium-high heat. Scrape the browning from the bottom of the roasting pan into the pot. Add the water, peppercorns, and bouquet garni. Bring to a boil, then reduce the heat to low. Simmer, uncovered, for 3 hours. Top up with a little water from time to time.

4. Remove from the heat. Set aside to cool for 30 mins.

5. Place a fine-mesh sieve over a large bowl. Carefully strain the stock into the bowl. Discard the bouquet garni, vegetables, and beef bones. Let the stock cool completely for 2-3 hours.

6. Use as directed in the recipes.

Nutritional Information/1L Serving

Energy	Protein	Carbo-hydrate	Fat	Saturated Fat	Sodium	Fibre
47 kcal	4.4g	1.2g	2.7g	1.1g	0.2g	0.3g

CHICKEN STOCK

Makes 3 litres | Prep. time 10 minutes | Cook time 2 hours | Cooling 30 minutes

Making stock at home is very easy but it does take some time to cook. The good thing is that you can make a large batch and either store in the refrigerator for several days, or freeze it for up to two months. When freezing, pour the stock into small containers and freeze. Once solid, place the individual blocks of stock in a large plastic freezer bag to use as required.

1½ kg chicken

4 litres cold water

1 onion, chopped

1 carrot, chopped

1 leek, chopped

2 bay leaves

2-3 springs fresh thyme

Small bunch fresh parsley

8 black peppercorns

Salt

1. Rinse the chicken thoroughly inside and out and place in a large soup pot with water. Add the onion, carrot, leek, bay leaves, thyme, parsley, peppercorns, and salt.

2. Bring to a boil over medium heat. Use a slotted spoon to remove any scum that rises to the surface. Reduce the heat to low and simmer, uncovered, for 2 hours, skimming the surface every 30 mins. Top up with a little water from time to time.

3. Remove from the heat. Set aside to cool for 30 mins.

4. Place a fine-mesh sieve over a large bowl. Carefully strain the stock into the bowl. Discard the herbs and vegetables. Reserve the cooked chicken meat for use in salads, burgers, or pies. Let the stock cool completely, then chill overnight.

5. When ready to use, scoop the fat off the tops with a large spoon and discard. Use as directed in the recipes.

Nutritional Information/1L Serving

Energy	Protein	Carbo-hydrate	Fat	Saturated Fat	Sodium	Fibre
190 kcal	37.0g	1.0g	4.1g	2.0g	5.1g	5.1g

VEGETABLE STOCK

Makes
2
litres

Prep. time
10
minutes

Cook time
2
hours

Cooling
30
minutes

Homemade stock tastes so much better than stock made from stock or bouillon cubes. Making stock at home allows you to control the amount of salt, which is ideal if you are following a low-sodium diet.

2 tbsp extra-virgin olive oil

2 large onions, coarsely chopped

1 turnip, peeled and coarsely chopped

2 carrots, peeled and coarsely chopped

4 stalks celery, coarsely chopped

Salt

3 litres cold water + extra, to top up

Small bunch fresh parsley

12 whole black peppercorns

3 dried bay leaves

1. Heat the oil in a large soup pot over medium-high heat. Add the onions, turnips, carrots, and celery, and sauté until lightly browned, about 5 mins. Season with salt.

2. Add the water, parsley, peppercorns, and bay leaves and bring to a boil. Use a slotted spoon to remove any scum that rises to the surface. Reduce the heat to low and simmer, uncovered, for 2 hours. Skimming the surface every 30 mins or so. Top up with a little water from time to time.

3. Remove from the heat. Set aside to cool for 30 mins.

4. Place a fine-mesh sieve over a large bowl. Discard the solids in the sieve. Let cool to room temperature.

5. Cover the stock with plastic wrap (cling film) or place in an airtight container and store in the refrigerator. Use as directed in the recipes.

Nutritional Information/1L Serving

	Energy	Protein	Carbo-hydrate	Fat	Saturated Fat	Sodium	Fibre
	76 kcal	1.1g	4.4g	5.6g	4.4g	3.8g	0.4g

MULLIGATAWNY SOUP

1 pack Slim Rice

1 small onion, chopped

2 stalks celery, chopped

1 carrot, diced

50g butter

1½ tablespoons plain flour

1½ teaspoons curry powder

1 litre chicken stock

½ apple - peeled, cored and chopped

1 skinless, boneless chicken breast fillet, diced

salt and freshly ground black pepper to taste

1 pinch dried thyme

100ml double cream

1. Prepare Slim Rice as per package instructions (drained and rinsed).
2. Sauté onions, celery, carrot and butter in a large soup pot.
3. Add flour and curry powder and cook for 5 more minutes.
4. Add chicken stock, mix well and bring to the boil. Simmer for about ½ hour.
5. Add apple, rice, chicken, salt, pepper and thyme. Simmer 15 to 20 minutes.
6. Stir in cream, garnish with fresh thyme (optional) and serve.

Nutritional Information/Serving

Energy	Protein	Carbo-hydrate	Fat	Saturated Fat	Sodium	Fibre
374 kcal	27.0g	12.0g	22.5g	13.7g	1.9g	6.4g

CHICKEN NOODLE SOUP

Serves **2** · Prep. time **15** minutes · Cook time **10** minutes

1 pack of Slim Pasta Fettucini or Noodles

2 tsp vegetable oil

5 large spring onions, trimmed, roughly sliced on the diagonal

1 onion, chopped

2 garlic cloves, roughly chopped

2cm piece ginger, finely chopped

1 red chilli, seeded, sliced into thin strips

1 head pak choi, white and green parts separated, finely chopped

pinch salt

2 chicken thighs, skin and bones removed, cut into strips

1 pinch ground allspice

1 litre hot chicken stock

1 dash soy sauce

1 stalk lemongrass, lightly crushed with the edge of a knife

2 tbsp chopped fresh coriander

1. Heat the oil in a frying pan over a medium heat. Add the spring onion, onion, garlic, ginger and chilli and fry for 2-3 minutes, or until the onions have softened slightly.

2. Add the white shreds of pak choi and the salt. Continue to fry for 3-4 minutes, or until the pak choi has wilted.

3. Add the chicken strips and ground allspice and stir until the ingredients are well combined and coated in the allspice. Continue to fry for 2-3 minutes, or until the spices are fragrant.

4. Add the chicken stock and soy sauce to the pan. Bring to the boil and cook for 3-4 minutes.

5. Prepare Slim Pasta Fettucini or Noodles as per package instructions (drained and rinsed).

6. Add the green shreds of pak choi, pasta or noodles and lemongrass stalk and stir well. Continue to boil the mixture for 4-5 minutes, or until the noodles are tender and the chicken is completely cooked through. Just before serving, stir in the chopped coriander.

7. Serve in bowls at once.

Nutritional Information/Serving

Energy	Protein	Carbo-hydrate	Fat	Saturated Fat	Sodium	Fibre
225 kcal	22.5g	4.0g	12.3g	2.0g	1.4g	4.5g

HOT AND SOUR PRAWN SOUP

1 pack Slim Noodles

700ml chicken stock

1 lemongrass stalk, bruised and cut into large pieces

5 thick slices galangal

6 coriander stems, bruised, plus leaves to garnish

3 lime leaves, torn

6 large prawns, shelled

3 tbsp Thai fish sauce

2 small green chillies, chopped

4 tbsp lime juice

2 whole dried red chillies to garnish (for flavour)

1. Prepare Slim Noodles as per package instructions (drained and rinsed).
2. Bring the stock to a boil in a medium-sized saucepan.
3. Add the lemongrass, galangal, coriander roots and lime leaves, then simmer for 2 mins.
4. Add the noodles, prawns, fish sauce, chillies and lime juice, then return to the boil.
5. Taste and adjust the seasoning with either more lime juice or fish sauce then garnish with coriander leaves and whole red chillies and serve.

Nutritional Information/Serving

Energy	Protein	Carbo-hydrate	Fat	Saturated Fat	Sodium	Fibre
144 kcal	25.0g	3.0g	2.1g	0.9g	2.4g	6.5g

WANTON NOODLE SOUP

1 pack of Slim Noodles and Fettucini

450g ground pork

2 stalks spring onion, finely minced

1 stalk spring onion, finely chopped for garnish

4 mushrooms, sliced

1 tbsp soy sauce

1 tsp rice vinegar

1 tsp cornstarch

¼ tsp sugar

1½ tsp sesame oil

200g wonton wrappers, at room temperature, covered with a damp towel

1 tbsp cornstarch + ¼ cup cool water (cornstarch slurry)

1½ litre chicken stock

1 red chilli, seeded and chopped for garnish

chilli garlic sauce (optional)

1. In a large bowl, combine the pork, soy sauce, rice vinegar, cornstarch, sugar and 1 tsp sesame oil. Mix well. Put a teaspoon of filling in the middle of a wonton wrapper, brush cornstarch slurry on all edges. Fold over to form a triangle, press to secure edges, encasing the filling. Brush cornstarch slurry on one tip of the triangle. Bring two corners together and press to secure. Place on clean, dry plate in one layer and cover loosely with plastic wrap to prevent drying. Repeat with remaining.

2. In a large stockpot, add all but 2 cups of the stock and bring to a boil. Turn the heat to medium-high and add the wontons. Bring pot back to a gentle boil. When it reaches a boil, add 1 cup of the reserved stock. Bring back to a boil and add the remaining 1 cup of reserved stock.

3. Keep the heat of the pot on. Scoop up the wontons and distribute amongst the bowls.

4. Prepare the Slim Noodles or Fettucini as per package instructions (drained and rinsed) and add to the stock to heat. Add mushrooms and let simmer, until cooked through. Ladle broth, noodles and mushrooms to bowls. Drizzle just a few drops of sesame oil in each bowl.

5. Garnish with spring onions and red chilli, and serve with chilli garlic sauce.

Nutritional Information/Serving

Energy	Protein	Carbo-hydrate	Fat	Saturated Fat	Sodium	Fibre
505 kcal	32.0g	22.0g	30.9g	10.3g	1.8g	4.4g

TOM YUM GOONG

1 pack of Slim Rice

2 tbsp Thai red curry paste

400ml (1 can) coconut milk

200g (1 tin) sweetcorn

16 cherry tomatoes

1 red chilli, seeded and thinly sliced

250g raw shrimps, head removed and peeled

500ml boiling chicken stock

4 tbsp coarsely chopped fresh coriander

1. Heat the red curry paste in a soup pot over medium heat until it starts to sizzle in its own oil.

2. Stir in the coconut milk and bring to a gentle simmer.

3. Prepare the Slim Rice as per package instructions (drained and rinsed).

4. Add corn and simmer for 3-4 minutes. Add the rice, cherry tomatoes, chilli, and shrimp and simmer for another 3-4 minutes.

5. Add chicken stock and stir in the coriander.

6. Ladle into four serving bowls, and serve hot.

Nutritional Information/Serving

Energy	Protein	Carbo-hydrate	Fat	Saturated Fat	Sodium	Fibre
216 kcal	22.0g	10.0g	9.1g	7.2g	0.9g	4.4g

LENTIL AND BACON SOUP

Lentils are a good source of lean protein, as well as a dietary fibre, vitamin B1, and several minerals.

1 pack of Slim Rice

2 tbsp extra-virgin olive oil

1 onion, finely chopped

150g pancetta, cut into small cubes

1 carrot, cut into small cubes

1 tsp ground cumin

½ tsp ground turmeric

2 cloves garlic, finely chopped

1 chilli, seeded and finely chopped

1½ litres chicken stock

250g red lentils

1 tbsp coarsely chopped fresh parsley to serve

1. Heat the oil in a soup pot over low heat. Add onion, half pancetta, and the carrot. Simmer until the vegetables are softened, 7-10 mins.

2. Add cumin, turmeric, garlic, and chilli and cook until aromatic, 2-3 minutes.

3. Pour in the chicken stock and add the lentils. Bring to a boil, then cover, and simmer over low heat, stirring occasionally, until the lentils are tender, 20-25mins.

4. Prepare the Slim Rice as per package instructions (drained and rinsed).

5. Add rice to soup and mix thoroughly.

6. Just before the soup is ready, dry-fry the remaining pancetta in a small frying pan over medium heat until crisp and golden.

7. Ladle the soup into serving bowls, sprinkle with the fried pancetta and the parsley, and serve hot.

Nutritional Information/Serving

Energy	Protein	Carbo-hydrate	Fat	Saturated Fat	Sodium	Fibre
360 kcal	26.0g	15.0g	25.0g	6.5g	2.4g	5.9g

GEORGIAN KHARCHO

Serves
6

Prep. time
10
minutes

Cook time
1.5
hours

750g lamb short ribs cut into 2.5cm pieces

1 pack (200g) Slim Rice

65g chopped walnuts

½ tsp paprika

½ tsp fresh & chopped cilantro

50g cherries dried

¼ tsp thyme

1 tbsp chopped parsley for garnish

3 tbsp sunflower oil

1 litre water

1 celery stick

1 carrot sliced

½ tsp black pepper

2 chopped medium onions

3 bay leaves

4 tbsp ketchup

¼ tbsp hot sauce

1 tsp sugar

2 tbsp fresh lemon juice

¼ tsp sage

2 tsp salt

3 minced garlic cloves

80ml dry red wine

1. Brown lamb pieces in sunflower oil with garlic. Remove from heat.

2. Bring water to a boil in a large stock pot. Add lamb, 1 teaspoon of salt and reduce heat to cook at slow boil for 30 minutes.

3. Prepare the Slim Rice as per package instructions (drained and rinsed).

4. Add Rice and all other ingredients, cook for 15 minutes at a slow boil, then reduce to simmer and cook for 30 minutes.

5. Serve garnished with chopped herbs.

Nutritional Information/Serving

Energy	Protein	Carbo-hydrate	Fat	Saturated Fat	Sodium	Fibre
362 kcal	28.0g	14.0g	20.6g	3.9g	0.3g	3.0g

ITALIAN MEATBALL SOUP

Serves
6

Prep. time
20
minutes

Cook time
15–20
minutes

1 pack of Slim Noodles

500g lean pork, minced

2 cloves garlic, finely chopped

1 small onion, finely chopped

4 tbsp finely chopped fresh parsley

½ tsp red pepper flakes

150g fine dry bread crumbs

60g freshly grated parmesan + extra, to serve

Salt and freshly ground black pepper

2 tbsp extra-virgin olive oil

1.5 litres chicken stock

1. Combine the pork, garlic, onion, 2 tbsp of parsley, red pepper flake, bread crumbs, and Parmesan in a bowl. Season with salt and pepper. Mix well, then shape into small meatballs.

2. Heat the oil in a large frying pan over medium-low heat. Fry the meatballs until golden brown, 8-10 mins. Let drain on paper towels.

3. Prepare the Slim Noodles as per package instructions (drained and rinsed). Cut into shorter pieces (around 7-8 cm).

4. Add the chicken stock to the same pan and bring to a boil.

5. Add the noodles and meatballs and simmer gently over low heat for 2-3 mins.

6. Ladle the soup into serving bowls and garnish with remaining 2 tbsp of parsley and the extra Parmesan. Serve hot.

Nutritional Information/Serving

Energy	Protein	Carbo-hydrate	Fat	Saturated Fat	Sodium	Fibre
224 kcal	22.0g	5.0g	12.1g	4.3g	0.1g	1.9g

 CH

Borsch originally comes from Ukraine, but it is popular in many Eastern and Central European countries. These are several variations on the recipe, but beets are the key ingredient, giving the soup its characteristic colour and flavour.

1 pack of Slim Rice/Noodles

500g beetroot, peeled and quartered

1 carrot, peeled and chopped

1 parsnip, peeled and cut into chunks

1 leek, white part only, sliced

1 onion, chopped

90ml, freshly squeezed lemon juice

½ tsp allspice

½ tsp nutmeg

3 bay leaves

1½ litres beef stock

Salt and freshly ground black pepper

250ml sour cream

4 tbsp chopped fresh dill

Rye bread to serve

1. Put the beets, carrots, parsnip, leek, onion, lemon juice, allspice, nutmeg, and bay leaves in a soup pot with the beef stock. Bring to boil, the decrease the heat to low and simmer, partially covered, for 2 hours.

2. Meanwhile, prepare the Slim Rice/Noodles as per package instructions (drained and rinsed).

3. Remove from the heat, add rice or noodles, then puree with a hand-held blender. Season with salt and pepper.

4. Return the soup to low heat and simmer for 2-3 minutes until heated through, stirring occasionally. Ladle into bowls and garnish with sour cream and dill. Serve hot with rye bread.

Nutritional Information/Serving

Energy	Protein	Carbo-hydrate	Fat	Saturated Fat	Sodium	Fibre
195 kcal	10.0g	15.0g	3.9g	1.7g	0.9g	6.0g

ACHO

Serves
6

Prep. time
20
minutes

Cook time
5
minutes

Chill time
2–3
hours

.ack of Slim Rice

6 large slices, day old, firm-textured bread, crusts removed

1½ kg ripe, fresh tomatoes

2 cucumbers, peeled, halved, and seeded

1 red bell pepper, halved, seeded

1 red onion, halved

1 clove garlic

120ml extra-virgin olive oil + extra to serve

1 tbsp sherry vinegar

1 tbsp freshly squeezed lemon juice

¼ tsp ground cumin

Salt and freshly ground pepper

2 stalks celery, with leaves attached

120ml blanched whole almonds, split (optional)

To garnish the gazpacho, just sprinkle a few of the vegetables, fried bread cubes, and almond over each serving. Place the rest in small bowls on the table for people to help themselves.

1. Cut three slices of bread into small cubes and set aside. Soak the remaining three slices of bread in a bowl of water for 10 minutes. Squeeze out the excess water and set aside.

2. Prepare the Slim Rice as per package instructions (drained and rinsed).

3. Cut a cross in the base of each tomato. Blanch in a pan of boiling water for 10 seconds. Let cool for a few mins, then slip off the skins. Chop coarsely.

4. Coarsely chop one of the cucumbers, half the bell pepper, and half the onion, and add to the tomatoes.

5. Process the soaked bread and garlic in a food processor until a paste forms. Add the tomatoes and coarsely chopped vegetables and process until smooth.

6. With the motor running, gradually add 90ml of oil, vinegar, lemon, and cumin. Add Slim Rice. Season with salt and pepper. Chill for at least 2-3 hrs or until ready to serve.

7. When ready to serve, finely chop the celery, the remaining cucumber, bell peppers, onion, keeping them separate.

8. Heat a small frying pan over medium heat. Add the almonds and cook, shaking the pan until golden. Set aside.

9. Heat the remaining oil in the same frying pan over medium heat. Add the bread cubes and cook, tossing until golden.

10. Serve gazpacho chilled, drizzled with extra oil, and sprinkled with the chopped vegetables, fried bread, and almonds.

Nutritional Information/Serving

Energy	Protein	Carbo-hydrate	Fat	Saturated Fat	Sodium	Fibre
317 kcal	5.0g	25.0g	22.0g	2.9g	0.6g	4.2g

CHICKEN LAKSA

Laksa soup is a spicy noodle soup often served in Malaysia, Singapore and Indonesia

Handy Hint: You can also replace chicken with tofu (veg option).

1 pack of Slim Noodles

2 tbsp laksa paste

4 cups of chicken stock

1 can (400ml) can coconut milk

2 chicken breasts, thinly sliced

1 tbsp freshly squeezed lime juice

1 tbsp Thai fish sauce

1 tsp brown sugar

1 cup (50g) fresh bean sprouts, to serve

2 spring onions, thinly sliced, to serve

fresh coriander to serve

1. Prepare the Slim Noodles as per package instructions (drained and rinsed).
2. Place a soup pot over medium heat. Add the laksa paste and stir until fragrant (1 min). Stir in chicken stock and coconut milk.
3. Bring to a simmer, add the chicken, simmer until just cooked through (5 mins).
4. Stir in the lime juice, fish sauce, brown sugar.
5. Heat noodles in hot water or in an open pan.
6. To serve, divide the noodles evenly among 4 large soup bowls. Ladle in the soup base and top with bean sprouts, spring onions and coriander, Serve immediately.

Nutritional Information/Serving

Energy	Protein	Carbo-hydrate	Fat	Saturated Fat	Sodium	Fibre
240 kcal	24.0g	6.0g	11.8g	10.0g	1.8g	4.1g

BEEF AND NOODLE SOUP

This Oriental-style soup is packed with flavour and sustenance. Serve hot as a complete meal in itself. Because the beef is cooked right at the end with the heat of the soup, make sure that it is very thinly sliced and that the soup you ladle over it is boiling hot.

1 pack Slim Pasta Spaghetti

1kg beef bones

3 litres cold water

2 large onions, chopped

5cm piece ginger, thinly sliced

5 star anise

2 cinnamon sticks

1 tsp back peppercorns

5 whole cloves

1 tbsp coriander seeds

2 tbsp Thai fish sauce

2 tbsp lime juice + wedges, to serve

Salt and freshly ground black pepper

250g beef fillet steak, very thinly sliced

100g bean sprouts

3 spring onions, thinly sliced

½ cup fresh mint leaves

½ cup coriander leaves

1 red chilli, thinly sliced

1. Place the beef bones, water, onions, ginger, star anise, cinnamon, peppercorns, cloves and coriander seeds in a large soup pot over high heat. Bring to boil, then decrease the heat to very low and simmer for 3 hrs, skimming the surface occasionally with a slotted spoon. The liquid should reduce by half.

2. Prepare the Slim Pasta Spaghetti as per package instructions (drained and rinsed). Cut spaghetti roughly in 5cm lengths with a kitchen scissors.

3. Remove from heat and strain through a fine mesh sieve into a clean pot. Remove and reserve any meat from the bones and discard the remaining solids.

4. Place the soup over high heat and bring to boil. Add the spaghetti, fish sauce and lime juice and stir to combine. Season with salt and pepper.

5. Place a few sliced beef and any reserved meat from bones into serving bowls. Ladle the soup into bowls, and top with bean sprouts, spring onions, chillies, mint and coriander, serve hot with lime wedges.

Nutritional Information/Serving

Energy	Protein	Carbo-hydrate	Fat	Saturated Fat	Sodium	Fibre
302 kcal	33.0g	9.0g	13.6g	5.6g	0.9g	3.1g

ALL'AMATRICANA

1 pack of Slim Pasta Spaghetti

2 tbsp of olive oil

1 small onion, finely chopped

125g of pancetta, cut into small, thin strips

1 fresh red chilli, seeded and chopped

500g tinned tomatoes, chopped

1 tbsp fresh flat-parsely, chopped (optional)

1. Prepare the Slim Pasta Spaghetti as per package instructions (drained and rinsed).

2. Sauté the pancetta in a large frying pan over medium heat until lightly brown. Add the onion and sauté until softened,

3. Add the tomatoes and chilli, simmer over medium heat to thicken the sauce.

4. Add the pasta to sauce and mix well. Toss gently and serve hot, garnish with parsley.

Nutritional Information/Serving

Energy	Protein	Carbo-hydrate	Fat	Saturated Fat	Sodium	Fibre
420 kcal	14.0g	12.0g	34.0g	10.0g	0.8g	4.2g

ALLA CARBONARA

Alla Carbonara is a traditional dish from the Eternal City of Rome. The sauce is thought to have been invented at the end of World War II when Allied troops arrived in the city with plenty of bacon and eggs. Local cooks used these ingredients to make this delicious sauce.

1 pack of Slim Pasta Fettucini or Spaghetti

2 tbsp of olive oil

1 small onion, finely chopped

¾ cup (75g) diced bacon

2 eggs

3 tbsp of heavy (double) cream

½ cup (45g) freshly ground Pecorino or Parmesan cheese

1. Prepare the Slim Pasta Fettucini as per package instructions (drained and rinsed).

2. Heat oil in a pan over medium heat. Add onion and sauté until pale gold. Add the bacon and sauté until crisp. Set aside.

3. Beat the eggs and cream in a large bowl. Season with salt and pepper and sprinkle with cheese.

4. Add the pasta to the pan with bacon. Return to high heat, add the egg mixture, toss briefly so that the eggs cook lightly but are still creamy.

5. Season with extra black pepper and serve immediately.

Nutritional Information/Serving

Energy	Protein	Carbo-hydrate	Fat	Saturated Fat	Sodium	Fibre
430 kcal	22.0g	5.0g	35.0g	12.0g	1.4g	2.5g

AUTHENTIC ITALIAN LASAGNE

This is one of the best-loved and much-imitated of all Italian pasta dishes.

1 pack (200g) Slim Pasta lasagne sheets

1 onion, chopped

1 carrot, chopped

1 stick celery, chopped

Pinch dried marjoram

55g dried porcini mushrooms, softened in hot water, drained and chopped

3 tbsp olive

225g stewing veal, minced coarsely

55g prosciutto crudo, chopped

1 tbsp plain flour

1 large glass red wine

¼ tsp freshly ground nutmeg

350ml thick passata

110g chicken livers, sautéd in butter until just browned

540ml béchamel sauce

110g freshly grated Parmesan

1. Prepare the Slim Lasagne sheets as per package instructions (drained and rinsed).
2. Fry vegetables and mushrooms together gently in a large pot with oil until soft.
3. Add veal, and prosciutto and cook gently until browned. Add flour and stir until it is absorbed.
4. Raise heat and add red wine, stirring for 2 minutes before lowering heat and adding nutmeg and passata. Simmer gently for an hour, stirring occasionally. Remove from heat and add chicken livers.
5. Butter a medium oven-proof dish and cover the bottom with a layer of pasta sheets. Cover with meat sauce, and then layer béchamel sauce. Continue this way until you have filled the dish and used up all the ingredients, ending with a layer of pasta covered with Parmesan cheese.
6. Bake in a pre-heated oven at 180°C until golden brown and bubbling hot. Leave to stand for at least 5 minutes before serving.

Nutritional Information/Serving

Energy	Protein	Carbo-hydrate	Fat	Saturated Fat	Sodium	Fibre
458 kcal	34.0g	22.0g	21.0g	10.0g	1.6g	5.5g

CREAMY CHICKEN & MUSHROOM FETTUCINI

Serves	Prep. time	Cook time
2	10 minutes	20 minutes

Fettucini or tagliatelle is one of my favourite pasta shapes - they are basically wide ribbons of pasta that perfectly suit rich pasta sauces like this one.

1 pack (200g) Slim Pasta Fettucini

½ tbsp salted butter

1 tbsp plain flour

300ml (1 cup) whole milk

2 tbsp of olive oil

1 chicken breast cubed

4 mushrooms sliced

2 shallots, chopped

5 sage leaves , chopped

25 grams of parmesan

Fresh oregano to garnish

1. Prepare the Slim Pasta Fettucini as per package instructions (drained and rinsed).

2. Melt the butter in a saucepan until foaming, stir in the flour until smooth, then add milk and stir again. Simmer until thickened. Add the cheese and stir until well blended. Season with salt and pepper to taste.

3. Heat oil in a pan over medium heat. Add shallots, chicken and mushrooms until cooked, then add fettucini to heat for 2 minutes. Add sage leaves then the white sauce and stir well.

4. Garnish with fresh oregano and cracked pepper. Serve and enjoy.

Nutritional Information/Serving

Energy	Protein	Carbo-hydrate	Fat	Saturated Fat	Sodium	Fibre
430 kcal	31.0g	9.0g	29.0g	11.0g	0.45g	3.0g

FETTUCINE WITH CREAMY SPINACH

Serves 2

Prep. time 5 minutes

Cook time 5 minutes

Although you can use any shape of pasta you like for this sauce, the fettucini shape holds the creamy sauce perfectly. A great sauce with a wonderful color.

1 pack (200g) Slim Pasta Fettucini

1kg fresh spinach leaves

8 tbsp light or whipping cream

6 tbsp freshly grated Parmesan cheese, plus extra to serve

¼ tsp grated nutmeg

Salt and freshly ground black pepper

1 tbsp butter

1 tbsp Ricotta cheese

1. Wash the spinach thoroughly, then cram it into a large saucepan with just the water clinging to the leaves. Put the lid on the saucepan and place over a low heat for about 5 minutes, until all the leaves have wilted.

2. Drain well, squeezing out any excess liquid, then put the cooked spinach in the food processor with cream, butter and Parmesan. Stir in the nutmeg and season to taste.

3. Prepare the Slim Pasta Fettucini as per package instructions (drained and rinsed).

4. Dry fry in an open pan and pour over the sauce and toss together.

5. Serve with a dollop ricotta cheese, and sprinkle a little Parmesan.

Nutritional Information/Serving

Energy	Protein	Carbo-hydrate	Fat	Saturated Fat	Sodium	Fibre
436 kcal	25.0g	10.0g	31.0g	23.0g	0.7g	12.0g

WHEAT FREE

GLUTEN FREE

...OOM AND
...NA FETTUCINI

1 pack (200g) Slim Pasta Fettucini

320g (1 tin) tuna

20g butter

90g mushrooms, sliced (mix a few varieties)

120ml cream

2 tbsp tomato paste

1 tbsp parsley, chopped

4 fresh plum tomatoes, halved

1 onion, chopped

1. Melt butter over medium heat and stir in chopped onion until onion is brown. Add drained tuna and stir.

2. Stir in mushrooms and tomato paste. Add salt and pepper, cream and parsley. Add plum tomatoes. Cook until mushrooms are soft.

3. Prepare the Slim Pasta Fettucini as per package instructions (drained and rinsed).

4. Add to the tuna and mushroom sauce. Turn using tongs to heat the pasta.

5. Serve and garnish with parsley.

Nutritional Information/Serving

Energy	Protein	Carbo-hydrate	Fat	Saturated Fat	Sodium	Fibre
452 kcal	47.0g	13.0g	21.0g	13.0g	1.1g	5.0g

...NE WITH
...VOCADO & RICOTTA

This pasta dish is dressed with a lovely pale green sauce that requires no cooking at all.
Ideal for hot summer days.

1 pack of Slim Pasta Penne

1 ripe avocados, peeled and mashed

4 tbsp fresh ricotta cheese

1 tbsp whole milk or single cream

Salt and freshly ground black pepper

1 tbsp fresh flat-leaf parsley, chopped

Freshly grated Parmesan cheese, to serve

1. Prepare the Slim Pasta Penne as per package instructions (drained and rinsed).
2. Beat the mashed avocado with ricotta cheese and milk or half and half to make a fairly smooth sauce. Season with salt and pepper, then stir in the parsley.
3. Add the pasta and toss together thoroughly, adding a little water if required. Chill for at least 2 hours before serving.
4. Serve with freshly grated Parmesan cheese separately.

Nutritional Information/Serving

Energy	Protein	Carbo-hydrate	Fat	Saturated Fat	Sodium	Fibre
212 kcal	3.9g	2.4g	20.0g	26.0g	0.2g	4.5g

PENNE ARABIATA

Cheese is not normally served with this recipe. However if you insist on having cheese it has to be aged, peppery pecorino.

1 pack (200g) Slim Pasta Penne
2 tbsp of olive oil
2 cloves garlic, peeled and finely chopped
1 to 2 dried red chillies
500g tinned tomatoes, chopped
4 to 5 large basil leaves, hand torn
1 tbsp fresh flat-parsely, chopped

1. Prepare the Slim Pasta Penne as per package instructions (drained and rinsed).
2. Fry the garlic and chilli in olive oil until they are slightly blackened. Discard the chilli and add tomatoes to the pan. Season with salt and simmer for 20 minutes. (Optional - add a tsp of sugar to enhance the flavor of tomatoes)
3. In an open pan dry fry the penne for 2 minutes. This will heat the penne and remove any surface water.
4. Pour over the sauce and mix together, add basil.
5. Garnish with parsley and enjoy.

Nutritional Information/Serving

 WHEAT FREE
 GLUTEN FREE
 DIARY FREE

Energy	Protein	Carbo-hydrate	Fat	Saturated Fat	Sodium	Fibre
189 kcal	3.0g	8.0g	15.0g	2.1g	1.0g	3.7g

PESTO, POTATOES & GREEN BEAN FETTUCINE

Pesto is another classic pasta sause. It comes originally from the northern city of Genova, where the mild Mediterranean climate is perfect for growing fresh herbs most of the year. In Genova, spaghetti or fettucini are traditionally served with pesto, small cubes of potatoes and green beans.

1 pack (200g) Slim Pasta Fettucini or Spaghetti

200g green beans

4 small new potatoes, cut into small cubes

Parmesan cheese cut into slices (for garnish)

Fresh basil leaves, to garnish

1. Prepare the Slim Pasta Fettucini as per package instructions (drained and rinsed).
2. Cook the green beans in boiling water (salted) until almost tender. Remove from cooking and set aside.
3. Cook potatoes till tender. Remove and set aside.
4. Dry the rinsed pasta using kitchen towel and put into a large bowl.
5. Add the pesto, green beans, and potatoes to pasta. Season with pepper. Sprinkle with Parmesan and garnish with basil and pine nuts. Serve hot or cold.

Pesto

2 cups (100g) fresh basil leaves

2 garlic, coarsely chopped

½ tsp salt

½ cup pine nuts lightly toasted (+ extra toasted to garnish)

⅓ cup (50g) freshly grated Parmesan cheese

⅓ cup (50g) freshly grated pecorino cheese

½ cup (120ml) extra virgin olive oil

(Refrigerate extra in a glass jar for future use)

1. Combine the basil, garlic, and salt in a food processor and blend for 5 seconds. Add the pine nuts, both cheeses, and half the oil and blend for 5 more seconds. Add the remainder oil and blend to form a smooth pesto.

Nutritional Information/Serving

Energy	Protein	Carbo-hydrate	Fat	Saturated Fat	Sodium	Fibre
414 kcal	5.0g	10.0g	38.0g	5.4g	1.4g	5.7g

SEAFOOD LEMON PEPPER SPAGHETTI

This is a fishy version of the classic bacon and cheese version and it's just as tasty!

1 pack (200g) Spaghetti/Penne/Fettucini
2 spring onions, finely chopped
2 lemons, juice and rind
3 tbsp olive oil
300g baby squid, cleaned and cut into small pieces
4 tbsp dry white wine
300g skinless cod fillet, cubed
300g cooked mussels, shelled
3 eggs
1 tbsp fresh parsley, chopped
25g Parmesan

1. Prepare the Slim Pasta as per package instructions (drained and rinsed).

2. Sauté spring onions gently in olive oil for 5 minutes. Add baby squid stir for 2 to 3 minutes, then add wine and allow alcohol to evaporate, then cover and simmer gently for 15 minutes or until squid is completely cooked. Season with pepper.

3. Once squid is tender, add the cod and mussels, heat through and stir in parsley. Season to taste. Beat eggs and Parmesan cheese in a bowl.

4. Dry fry the pasta in a pan, add the eggs and mix together to just cook the eggs and then add squid, mussels and fish mixture. Add lemon juice and rind and mix thoroughly for 1 to 2 minutes before serving.

5. Garnish with parsley and season with salt and pepper.

Nutritional Information/Serving

Energy	Protein	Carbo-hydrate	Fat	Saturated Fat	Sodium	Fibre
684 kcal	76.0g	8.0g	38.0g	7.5g	2.8g	7.8g

SPAGHETTI AND MEATBALLS

Serves
2–3

Prep. time
15
minutes

Cook time
1.5
hours

1 pack (200g) Slim Pasta Spaghetti/
Penne

60ml olive oil

½ green pepper, cut into small
squares

½ onion, chopped

225g minced pork

1 egg, beaten

1 clove garlic, chopped finely

fresh basil leaves, roughly torn

3 to 4 tbsp fine, dry breadcrumbs

375ml of passata

handful mixed fresh herbs,
chopped finely

1. Fry onion in olive oil until softened but
   not browned, set aside.

2. Mix pork with eggs, seasoning, garlic,
   parsley, and 2 to 3 tbsp breadcrumbs.
   With wet hands, shape the mixture into
   meatballs about the size of large olives,
   roll in the remaining breadcrumbs. Gently
   reheat the onion and oil mix and fry the
   meatballs for about 2 minutes to seal.

3. Drain of any excess oil and add passata
   and chopped mixed herbs. Simmer
   together for about an hour, stirring
   frequently. Add chopped green peppers
   just before the next steps.

4. Prepare the Slim Pasta as per package
   instructions (drained and rinsed).

5. Add pasta to the meat and sauce.
   Mix gently.

6. Serve and garnish with basil.

Nutritional Information/Serving

Energy	Protein	Carbo-hydrate	Fat	Saturated Fat	Sodium	Fibre
504 kcal	16.0g	15.0g	41.0g	10.0g	0.6g	3.0g

PRAWN AND CHILLI PASTA

1 pack (200g) Slim Pasta Spaghetti

250g fresh tomatoes, peeled and chopped

2 cloves garlic, chopped

4 tbsp olive oil

1 tsp concentrated tomato puree

250g prawns, peeled and deveined

150ml dry white wine

1 small dried red chilli, chopped finely

3 tbsp fresh parsley, chopped

4 sundried tomatoes soaked in hot water

salt and freshly ground black pepper

1. Drop tomatoes into boiling water for one minute, then peel and chop very roughly.

2. Put garlic and oil into a saucepan, heat together until sizzling and then add the tomatoes and the tomato puree. Stir together for a few minutes, then add prawns and seal for a minute, then add white wine and allow the alcohol to evaporate before lowering heat to a very low simmer.

3. Add chopped chillies, cover and simmer very slowly until prawns turn pink. Add sundried tomatoes.

4. Prepare the Slim Pasta Spaghetti as per package instructions (drained and rinsed).

5. Add pasta to the sauce and turn using tongs until pasta is heated.

6. Serve and garnish with parsley.

Nutritional Information/Serving

Energy	Protein	Carbo-hydrate	Fat	Saturated Fat	Sodium	Fibre
420 kcal	24.0g	7.0g	32.0g	4.3g	0.1g	4.3g

SPAGHETTI AL CRAB WITH CARBONARA SAUCE

Serves
2

Prep. time
5
minutes

Cook time
15
minutes

1 pack (200g) Slim Spaghetti or Fettucini

85g pancetta slices, finely chopped

2 tbsp unsalted butter

2 tbsp heavy cream

1 large egg, beaten

40g freshly grated parmesan cheese, more for serving

20g freshly grated pecorino cheese

100g fresh crabmeat

1. Prepare the Slim Pasta as per package instructions (drained and rinsed).

2. In a large, heavy skillet, sauté the pancetta over mediaum-low heat for 4 to 5 minutes. Add butter and cream, cook for further 3 minutes, stirring occasionally. Remove from heat.

3. Add pasta to the pancetta mixture, using tongs to thoroughly coat it with sauce.

4. Return pan to low heat and cook for 3 to 4 minutes to heat the pasta.

5. Crack the eggs over pasta and quickly toss to combine, using tongs. Stir in the cheeses until the eggs are cooked and cheese melted.

6. Remove from heat; add crabmeat and season with salt and pepper.

Nutritional Information/Serving

Energy	Protein	Carbo-hydrate	Fat	Saturated Fat	Sodium	Fibre
454 kcal	33.0g	1.0g	35.0g	19.0g	1.6g	1.8g

THYME
AD

1 pack (200g) Slim Pasta Spaghetti

125g tuna steak, cut into small pieces

2 tbsp plain flour

2 tbsp extra-virgin oil

1 clove garlic. Finely chopped

10 black olives, pitted and finely chopped

1 tbsp fresh thyme, finely chopped

1 fresh red or green chilli, seeded and finely chopped

1 small courgette, cut into small cubes

¼ cup (60ml) dry white wine

1. Prepare the Slim Pasta Spaghetti as per package instructions (drained and rinsed).
2. Toss the tuna on the flour, shaking to remove the excess.
3. Heat the oil in a large frying pan over medium heat. Add garlic, olives, chillies, and half of the thyme. Sauté until garlic is pale gold (2 mins)
4. Add tuna and courgettes. Sauté gently over medium heat until the tuna is cooked through (6 mins). Season with salt and black pepper.
5. Drizzle with wine and let it evaporate.
6. Dry fry spaghetti in an open pan to heat and add to the tuna sauce. Toss well. Garnish with remaining thyme and serve hot.

Nutritional Information/Serving

Energy	Protein	Carbo-hydrate	Fat	Saturated Fat	Sodium	Fibre
493 kcal	17.0g	5.0g	18.0g	2.6g	0.3g	3.6g

...RENG

This dish combines precooked meat and seafood. If you don't like meat, double up on the prawns or use a combination of prawns and mussels. Don't be put off by the long list of ingredients - it's a very easy dish to prepare.

2 packs (400g) of Slim Noodles

4 tbsp sunflower oil, divided

2 eggs, lightly beaten

3 tbsp soy sauce

1 chicken stock cube, crumbled

1 tsp medium curry powder

¼ tsp ground ginger

1 tsp sesame oil

175g cooked beef, pork or chicken, cut into strips

pinch sugar

4 spring onion, thinly sliced

½ green pepper. thinly sliced

½ red pepper, thinly sliced

4 pak choy leaves, chopped

75g bean sprouts

175g small prawns

1. Prepare Slim Noodles as per package instructions (drained and rinsed).

2. Heat 1 tbsp sunflower oil in a frying pan and add the beaten eggs. Cook like an omelette until set. Remove from pan and roll up, then cut into strips. Set aside in a warm place.

3. In a bowl, mix 1 tbsp sunflower oil, soy sauce, crumbed stock cube, curry powder, ground ginger, sesame oil and sugar. Set aside.

4. Heat the remaining oil in a large wok, then add the pak choy and stir-fry for 1 min, add the spring onions and peppers and stir-fry for another minute. Add the beef, pork or chicken and the prawns and stir-fry for 2 mins. Add the noodles and egg along with the bean sprouts and the soy sauce mixture and stir-fry to heat through, tossing to mix the ingredients evenly.

5. Serve hot.

Nutritional Information/Serving

Energy	Protein	Carbo-hydrate	Fat	Saturated Fat	Sodium	Fibre
353 kcal	24.0g	7.0g	23g	3.7g	2.3g	3.2g

YAKISOBA

 Serves 2
 Prep. time 10 minutes
 Cook time 20 minutes

Yakisoba is a classic Japanese street food made by stir-frying boiled ramen noodles, vegetables and meat or seafood with a sweet and savoury sauce.

In Japan, Yakisoba can be found sizzling away in stalls everywhere from baseball stadiums to traditional Omatsuri (festivals). If you've ever been to an event in Japan, you probably remember the smell of the fruity, spicy sauce caramelizing on giant teppan (cast iron griddles) with the noodles.

1 pack (200g) Slim Noodles

2 tbsp vegetable oil

4 shiitake mushrooms, sliced

200g pork belly, sliced

1 carrot, julienned (into sticks)

1 onion, sliced

100g cabbage, chopped

3 spring onions, sliced

Beni shoga (Japanese ginger pickle), for garnish

3 tbsp chuno sauce

½ tbsp oyster sauce

¼ tbsp ground white pepper

5g katsuobushi

Aonori (dried green seaweed) for garnish

1. Prepare Slim Noodles as per package instructions (drained and rinsed).

2. In a small bowl whisk together the chuno sauce, oyster sauce, and white pepper.

3. Heat 2 tbsp oil in a pan over medium-high heat until hot and then pan fry the pork and set aside.

4. In the same pan add carrots, onions and any tougher bits of cabbage. Stir-fry until the carrots are tender and then add the cabbage and spring onions. Continue stir-frying until cabbage is cooked.

5. Add the noodles and sauce, using tongs to lift and drop the noodles (like tossing a salad) to coat them evenly with sauce.

6. Sprinkle the katsuobushi onto the noodles, and continue tossing until the noodles are a uniform colour and you can smell the sauce starting to caramelize. Add the pork and toss.

7. Plate the yakisoba and sprinkle with aonori and beni shoga to garnish.

Nutritional Information/Serving

Energy	Protein	Carbo-hydrate	Fat	Saturated Fat	Sodium	Fibre
467 kcal	14.0g	15.0g	38.0g	12.0g	0.7g	3.9g

WANTON MEE

1 pack (200g) Slim Noodles

200g Chinese barbequed pork, thinly sliced

small bunch of Chinese mustard green, trimmed, cut in 5 cm length (separate the stems and leaves)

2 stalks spring onion, chopped

Sauce

4 tsp oyster sauce

1 tbsp dark sweet soy sauce

1 tbsp dark soy sauce

2 tsp toasted sesame oil

1 tbsp fried garlic oil (made from 8 cloves minced garlic in 8 tbsps cooking oil)

1. Heat oil in a pan over medium-low heat and stir in garlic until golden brown, Transfer to bowl and set aside.

2. In a small bowl add all the sauce ingredients and set aside.

3. Blanch the Chinese mustard greens in hot water, first the stems then add the leaves. Once wilted, drain well and set aside.

4. Prepare the Slim Noodles as per package instructions (drained and rinsed).

5. Heat noodles in an open pan and split into 2 serving bowls. Add the sauce to the noodles and mix evenly.

6. Top with pork and Chinese mustard green, spring onions and serve.

Nutritional Information/Serving

Energy	Protein	Carbo-hydrate	Fat	Saturated Fat	Sodium	Fibre
359 kcal	29.0g	14.0g	17.0g	0.8g	0.8g	4.9g

...ARIAN RAMEN ...OODLES

 Serves 2
 Prep. time 15 minutes
 Cook time 15 minutes

1 packs (200g) Slim Noodles

2 tsp toasted sesame oil (more for drizzling)

2 cloves garlic, minced

450ml vegetable broth

6 shiitake mushrooms, stemmed and thinly sliced

2 tsp miso paste

2 tsp soy sauce

3 spring onions, thinly sliced (use green part for garnish)

5cm wide roasted seaweed, cut crosswise in 8 strips

1 small carrot, julienned (into sticks)

75g bean sprouts

12 cherry tomatoes

100g Tofu, sliced into 6 pieces

1 small aubergine, thinly sliced diagonally

1. Drizzle Tofu, aubergine slices and tomatoes with sesame oil. Season with salt and pepper.

2. Heat a griddle pan and place the tofu (large sides down) to pan fry. Turn after a few minutes until golden brown on both the sides. Remove and set a side in warm place. Repeat the same with aubergine and tomatoes.

3. In a wok heat oil over medium-high heat, stir-fry garlic until fragrant, add carrots, mushrooms and spring onions and stir-fry until carrots are soft. Add broth, miso paste and soy sauce and bring to boil and add bean sprouts.

4. Meanwhile, prepare the Slim Noodles as per package instructions (drained and rinsed).

5. Divide noodles equally among large soup bowls and ladle soup over top. Divide the tofu, aubergine and tomatoes equally to the bowls.

6. Sprinkle with seaweed and garnish with green part of spring onions.

Nutritional Information/Serving

Energy	Protein	Carbo-hydrate	Fat	Saturated Fat	Sodium	Fibre
282 kcal	10.0g	13.0g	20.0g	4.7g	1.9g	7.2g

THAI NOODLES WITH CHICKEN

1 pack (200g) Slim Noodles

2 tbsp coconut oil

1 chicken breast, cubed

2 cloves garlic, crushed

2 stalks lemongrass, white part only finely chopped

½ tsp dried chilli flakes

1 bunch baby pak choy, sliced

1 tbsp fish sauce

1 tbsp brown sugar

1 lime, juiced

¼ cup coriander, chopped

1 small red pepper, cubed

1. Prepare the Slim Noodles as per package instructions (drained and rinsed).
2. In a bowl, combine fish sauce, brown sugar and lime juice.
3. Heat oil in a wok and stir-fry chicken until browned.
4. Add garlic, lemongrass and chilli and cook for 2 mins. Add pepper and pak choy and stir-fry for further 2 mins. Add noodles, stir, then add the sauce mix and heat through. Stir in coriander.
5. Serve hot. Serve red chilli flakes on the side.

Nutritional Information/Serving

Energy	Protein	Carbo-hydrate	Fat	Saturated Fat	Sodium	Fibre
260 kcal	21.0g	10.0g	15.0g	13.0g	0.3g	3.4g

THAI BEEF STIR FRIED NOODLES

If you're a fan of Asian noodles, be sure to try these Chinese-inspired Thai Beef Stir-Fried Noodles! This dish is super-delicious and also very healthy. The recipe is also quite flexible. Make it as spicy or mild as you like, and add your own choice of vegetables depending on what you have on hand.

275g beef, thinly sliced steak

1 pack (200g) of Slim Noodles

1 red bell pepper, thinly sliced

1 carrot, sliced

handful fresh basil

1 tsp sesame oil, to drizzle

2-3 tbsp coconut oil

75g mangetout

3 tbsp soy sauce

1 tsp brown sugar

1 shallot, minced

4-5 cloves garlic, finely chopped

5cm ginger, sliced thinly

1 fresh red chilli, sliced

5-7 fresh shiitake mushrooms, sliced

kaffir lime leaves, to garnish

Stir-fry Sauce

2/3 cup good-tasting chicken stock

3 tbsp oyster-flavoured sauce

3 tbsp cooking sherry

1 tbsp fish sauce

2 tsp brown sugar

½ tsp crushed chilli

2 tsp cornstarch

1. Stir together the soy sauce and brown sugar and pour over beef. Stir well and set aside to marinate.

2. Prepare the Slim Noodles as per package instructions (drained and rinsed).

3. Combine all stir fry sauce ingredients in a bowl, adding the cornstarch last and whisking to dissolve.

4. Heat a large wok over medium high heat. Add 2-3 tbsp oil and add the shallots, mangetout, garlic, ginger, and fresh chilli. Stir-fry 1-2 mins, then add the beef together with its marinade. Stir-fry 3 mins, or until beef is lightly cooked (add 2-3 tbsp stir-fry sauce in the process).

5. Add the carrots, continue stir-frying 1-2 minutes. Then add mushrooms and red peppers. Stir fry until vegetables have softened but are still bright.

6. Add noodles turning well while stir-frying. Cook till noodles have been heated. Add lime or lemon juice if required.

7. Serve and drizzle sesame oil, garnish with basil leaves and kaffir leaves.

Nutritional Information/Serving

Energy	Protein	Carbo-hydrate	Fat	Saturated Fat	Sodium	Fibre
352 kcal	26.0g	18.0g	18.0g	11.0g	1.4g	4.4g

SHRIMP PAD THAI

This is an authentic and very scrumptious recipe. The recipe is gleaned from what I've learned from Thai chefs in Thailand. The pad Thai sauce is so simple to put together, so don't be tempted to buy packaged Thai sauce.

1 pack (200g) of Slim Noodles

12 small to medium raw shrimp, shells removed

1 boneless chicken breast, chopped into small pieces

1 tbsp soy sauce

4 spring onions, sliced (keep white separate from green)

4 cloves garlic, minced

1 tsp grated galangal

1 fresh red chilli (finely sliced)

1 egg

100g bean sprouts

handful fresh coriander

40g dry roasted unsalted peanuts or cashew nuts, chopped

2 tbsp coconut oil

lime wedges for serving

Pad Thai Sauce

1 tbsp tamarind paste

60ml chicken stock

3 tbsp fish sauce

1 tbsp soy sauce

1/8 tsp ground white pepper

1 tbsp chilli sauce

4 tbsp palm sugar

1. Prepare the Slim Noodles as per package instructions (drained and rinsed).
2. Toss sliced chicken in 1 tbsp soy sauce and set aside.
3. In a small bowl, combine all the Pad Thai Sauce ingredients.
4. Heat a wok over medium-high heat. Add 2 tbsp oil and stir-fry the white parts of the onion, garlic, galangal, chilli for 1 min.
5. Add chicken and stir-fry for 2 mins. Add shrimps and continue stir-frying until shrimps are pink and plump.
6. Push ingredients aside and make a well. Crack an egg and stir-fry quickly to scramble.
7. Add noodles and drizzle one third of the Pad Thai sauce over them. Using tongs, gently stir-fry all the ingredients to heat the noodles. Keep adding the sauce.
8. Turn off heat. Fold in bean sprouts. Add the rest of Pad Thai sauce.
9. Sprinkle over the green onion, nuts and coriander, and garnish with lime wedges.

WHEAT FREE   DAIRY FREE

Nutritional Information/Serving

Energy	Protein	Carbo-hydrate	Fat	Saturated Fat	Sodium	Fibre
340 kcal	28.0g	14.0g	18.0g	11.0g	1.0g	3.2g

SHRIMP LO MEIN

 Serves 2–3
 Prep. time 20 minutes
 Cook time 15 minutes

1 pack (200g) Slim Noodles

200g raw shrimps, shelled and deveined

2 tsp Chinese rice wine

1 tsp cornstarch

4 tbsp vegetable oil

2 tsp sesame oil

1 red pepper, sliced

2 broccoli florets, prepared for stir-fry

½ cup Napa cabbage, shredded

2 cm ginger, minced

¼ cup chicken broth

1 tbsp oyster sauce

1 tbsp light soy sauce

½ tsp brown sugar

1. Prepare the Slim Noodles as per package instructions (drained and rinsed). Toss with sesame oil and set aside.

2. Add rice wine and cornstarch to the shrimps. Mix well and marinate for 15 mins.

3. In a bowl combine the sauce ingredients (chicken broth, ouster sauce, soy sauce and sugar) and set aside.

4. Heat wok over medium-high heat. Add 2 tbsp oil. Add ginger and stir-fry until aromatic. Add shrimp, stir-fry until they turn pink. Remove from wok and set aside in a warm place.

5. Heat 2 tbsp oil and add shredded cabbage and broccoli. Stir-fry for a minute and add red pepper. Stir-fry for another minute and remove from wok and set aside.

6. Using the same wok, over high heat, add the noodles and the sauce. Reduce heat to medium and toss to cover noodles in the sauce. Let sauce reduce, then add shrimp and vegetable back into the pan. Heat through and serve hot.

Nutritional Information/Serving

Energy	Protein	Carbo-hydrate	Fat	Saturated Fat	Sodium	Fibre
309 kcal	17.0g	8.0g	21.0g	2.9g	0.4g	4.3g

SEAFOOD STIR FRY

1 pack (200g) Slim Noodles

250g of mixed seafood (devein and remove shell if fresh)

2 tbsp olive oil

2 tbsp toasted sesame oil

4 tbsp dark soy sauce

2 red peppers, seeds removed and cut into thin strips

4 leeks, cut into strips

2 large onions, peeled and cut into thick wedges

4 garlic cloves, peeled and cut into slivers

a few sprigs of coriander

4 teaspoons balsamic vinegar

salt

1. Prepare the Slim Noodles as per package instructions (drained and rinsed).

2. In a wok heat 1 tbsp olive oil and 1 tbsp sesame oil. Stir-fry the peppers, onions and leeks until onions are golden brown. Remove from pan and set aside in a warm place.

3. Heat remaining oil in the same pan, add garlic and mixed seafood, cook over high heat until cooked through (8 mins if frozen and 4 min if fresh).

4. Mix in the noodles, reserved vegetables, balsamic vinegar and soy sauce. Turn using tongs to heat noodles.

5. Serve and garnish with coriander.

Nutritional Information/Serving

Energy	Protein	Carbo-hydrate	Fat	Saturated Fat	Sodium	Fibre
359 kcal	17.0g	21.0g	21.0g	3.0g	1.5g	6.2g

ILLI LEMON NOODLES WITH ASIAN SESAME PORK

1 pack (200g) Slim Noodles

25g sesame seeds

olive oil, for cooking

2 shallots, sliced

2 medium red chillies, halved, deseeded and very thinly sliced

zest and juice 1 lemon (using just half if it's very juicy)

½ red pepper, thinly sliced

2 spring onion, thinly sliced

5cm courgette, sliced

350g pork fillets, or loin, sliced into thin strips

knob of butter

drizzle sesame oil (optional)

100g mangetout, away tops and discard

1. Plunge mangetout into rapidly boiling salted water for 1 min before draining and keeping to one side.

2. Prepare the Slim Noodles as per package instructions (drained and rinsed).

3. Heat a wok, add the sesame seeds and toast until golden brown. Spoon into a bowl and set aside.

4. Season the pork with salt and pepper.

5. Add a splash of olive oil to the wok and stir-fry the pepper, spring onions, courgette, shallots, chilli and lemon zest over a medium heat until the shallots just begin to soften.

6. Increase the heat in the pan, add the pork and fry until the pork is golden brown.

7. Stir in the mangetout, sesame seeds, butter and lemon juice.

8. Add the noodles and using tongs turn well to heat noodles.

9. Finish with a drizzle of sesame oil and serve.

Nutritional Information/Serving

Energy	Protein	Carbo-hydrate	Fat	Saturated Fat	Sodium	Fibre
420 kcal	22.0g	8.0g	31.0g	7.5g	0.3g	6.1g

CHICKEN CHOW MEIN

This is such an easy dish to cook in a hurry. Use a dark soy sauce or a rich flavor or light soy for a brighter taste. If desired, you can use other vegetables such as mangetout, bamboo shoots, courgettes and thin green beans or thinly sliced carrots blanched for 1 minute before stir-frying.

Handy Hint: You can also replace chicken with tofu (veg option)

---

1 pack (200g) Slim Noodles

2 tbsp of toasted sesame oil
(sunflower oil can be used too)

1 chicken breast, cubed

3 -5 cm piece of ginger, finely grated

3 cups stir fry veg, finely chopped
(1 small carrot, 1 small bunch pak
choi, ½ red pepper, 4 mushrooms,
1 floret broccoli, 100g bean sprouts,
2 stocks spring onion, ½ onion,
sliced, baby corn)

4 tbsp dark soy sauce

1 fresh chilli (optional)

coriander for garnish

---

1. Prepare the Slim Noodles as per package instructions (drained and rinsed) and set aside.

2. Heat 2 tbsp of oil in a wok. Stir fry chicken until golden brown. Remove chicken from the wok.

3. Using the same wok over high heat, add ginger and vegetables. Stir fry for 2 minutes. Add 2 tbsp soy sauce. Remove the cooked vegetables.

4. Stir fry the noodles over high heat, for 2 minutes. Add the remainder of soy sauce. Toss thoroughly.

5. Mix chicken, vegetables and noodles. Add chilli and garnish with coriander before serving.

Nutritional Information/Serving

Energy	Protein	Carbo-hydrate	Fat	Saturated Fat	Sodium	Fibre
332 kcal	27.0g	14.0g	17.0g	2.7g	1.8g	6.9g

MEXICAN STIR FRY RICE

1 pack (200g) Slim Rice

2 tbsp sunflower oil

½ green pepper, diced

½ small onion, diced

1 cup cooked black beans, drained

2 tomatoes, diced

½ cup sweet corn

1 tbsp taco seasoning (cumin, chilli powder, garlic powder and cayenne)

hot sauce (optional)

1 avocado, seeded, peeled and chopped

10 olives, pitted and diced

2 jalapenos, diced (optional)

1. Prepare the Slim Rice as per package instructions (drained and rinsed).
2. Heat oil in a skillet, sauté green peppers and onion over medium heat (few minutes)
3. Add the rest of the ingredients and cook for 3 to 5 minutes. Spoon into a bowl and top with cheese, avocado, olives and jalapenos (optional).

Nutritional Information/Serving

Energy	Protein	Carbo-hydrate	Fat	Saturated Fat	Sodium	Fibre
261 kcal	6.0g	17.0g	16.3g	1.9g	0.5g	10.6g

CHICKEN CURRY & RICE

1 pack (200g) Slim Rice

4 skinless chicken thighs

1 onion, chopped

3 cloves garlic

1 inch stick of ginger

½ tsp of turmeric powder

2 medium tomatoes, chopped

½ tsp garam masala

2 tbsp oil

pinch sugar

½ tsp chilli powder

coriander leaves for garnish

1. Prepare the Slim Rice as per package instructions (drained and rinsed).

2. Blitz ginger and garlic in a food processor. Heat oil in a non-stick pan, add a pinch of sugar and caramelise.

3. Add onion and fry on high heat until golden brown. Add turmeric and chilli powder and fry for 2 minutes, then add tomatoes. Cook for 5 minutes, lower the heat and simmer.

4. Add chicken once tomatoes are cooked. Turn up the heat and stir vigorously to cover chicken with the paste. Add water to cover chicken, lower heat and stir occasionally until chicken is cooked.

5. Add garam masala and salt to taste.

6. Heat rice in hot water, drain and serve with chicken curry. Garnish with coriander.

Nutritional Information/Serving

Energy	Protein	Carbo-hydrate	Fat	Saturated Fat	Sodium	Fibre
486 kcal	46.0g	7.0g	28.7g	5.4g	0.5g	5.3g

VEGETABLE/CHICKEN STIR FRY WITH RICE

Serves 2

Prep. time 10 minutes

Cook time 15 minutes

Don't be put off by the long list of ingredients - it's a very easy dish to prepare.

Handy Hint: You can also replace chicken with tofu (veg option)

Ingredients
1 pack (200g) Slim Rice
3 tbsp of sesame oil, divided
2 eggs, lightly beaten
3 tbsp soy sauce
1 chicken stock cube, crumbled (veg cube for veg option)
1 tsp medium curry powder
½ tsp ground ginger
2 tbsp sesame oil
pinch sugar
4 spring onions, thinly sliced
½ green pepper, thinly sliced
½ red pepper, thinly sliced
1 chicken breast, (or tofu) cut into strips
75g bean sprouts

1. Prepare the Slim Rice as per package instructions (drained and rinsed).

2. Heat 1 tbsp of oil in a wok. Stir fry chicken until golden brown. Remove chicken from the wok.

3. Heat 1 tbsp of oil in a frying pan and add the beaten eggs. Cook like an omelette until set. Remove from pan and roll up, then cut into strips (keep warm).

4. In a bowl, mix, soy sauce, crumbled stock cube, curry powder, ground ginger, sesame oil and sugar. Set aside.

5. Heat the remainder of the oil in the wok over high heat. Stir fry onions and peppers for a minute. Add rice, egg, bean sprouts and the soy mixture. Stir fry to heat through, tossing to mix evenly.

6. Garnish with coriander (optional) and serve.

Chicken: Nutritional Information/Serving

Energy	Protein	Carbo-hydrate	Fat	Saturated Fat	Sodium	Fibre
444 kcal	30.0g	9.0g	31.0g	6.0g	2.7g	5.7g

Vegetarian: Nutritional Information/Serving

Energy	Protein	Carbo-hydrate	Fat	Saturated Fat	Sodium	Fibre
284 kcal	4.0g	9.0g	24.0g	4.2g	2.3g	5.7g

THAI FISH CURRY WITH RICE

1 pack (200g) Slim Rice

2 tbsp sunflower oil

1 shallot, chopped

1 clove garlic, crushed

1 small chilli, seeded and minced

1 tbsp thai red curry paste

½ lime, juiced

½ tbsp sugar

1 tbsp fish sauce

100ml fish stock

200ml coconut milk

250g white fish, cubed

50g prawns, peeled

4 Thai basil, fresh

4 coriander, fresh

1. Prepare the Slim Rice as per package instructions (drained and rinsed).

2. Heat oil in a frying pan, stir fry shallots and garlic until soft. Add chilli, curry paste, lime juice and sugar. Cook for 2 minutes then stir in fish sauce, stock and coconut milk.

3. Bring to a simmer, then add the fish and prawns and cook till prawns and fish are cooked through.

4. Serve on a bed of rice, garnish with Thai basil and coriander.

Nutritional Information/Serving

Energy	Protein	Carbo-hydrate	Fat	Saturated Fat	Sodium	Fibre
349 kcal	25.0g	6.0g	24.0g	8.8g	1.1g	4.8g

STEAK, ROASTED VEG KEBAB, RICE AND CURRY SAUCE

1 pack (200g) Slim Rice

260g steak

25g butter

6 button mushroom, halved

¼ onion, minced

½ tbsp curry power

1 tsp powdered coriander

2 tbsp whole milk

¼ apple, chopped

¼ cup beef broth

1 medium onion, slices into wedges

1 red pepper, cut into squares

½ green pepper, cut into squares

2 tbsp olive oil

1 lemon, juiced

3 garlic clove, minced

15g fresh thyme, chopped

15g fresh rosemary, chopped

Grilled Steak

1. Melt butter and sauté 2 garlic cloves and onions (minced) until golden brown. Stir in coriander and curry powder. Add milk and apple. Simmer for 10 min, stirring frequently.
2. Add broth and simmer for 15 mins.
3. While sauce is simmering, grill steak to desired level of "doneness". Brush with sauce and serve.

Veg Kebab

1. Prepare a BBQ for medium heat (or oven grill).
2. Thread mushrooms, onion and peppers on skewers.
3. In a small bowl, mix together olive oil, 1 garlic, lemon juice, thyme, rosemary, salt and pepper. Brush mushrooms and peppers with mixture.
4. Place kebabs on BBQ. Baste frequently with oil mixture. Cook until mushrooms are tender and thoroughly cooked. (add more broth if sauce gets too thick).

Assemble meal

1. Prepare the Slim Rice as per package instructions (drained and rinsed). Dry fry rice in an open pan. Add remaining sauce and heat until rice is hot.
2. Serve grilled steak, veg kebab and rice.

Nutritional Information/Serving

Energy	Protein	Carbo-hydrate	Fat	Saturated Fat	Sodium	Fibre
513 kcal	42.0g	10.0g	32.0g	10.0g	0.6g	6.5g

RICE AND FETA STUFFED PEPPERS

1 pack (200g) Slim Rice

4 medium bell peppers, tops cut off, and deseeded

1 tbsp olive oil, extra for spraying

1 garlic clove, minced

2 mushrooms, sliced

½ medium onion, chopped

1 tsp Italian seasoning

1 tbsp capers

8 olives, pitted and chopped

100g feta cheese, crumbled

4 stalks fresh parsley

6 large tomatoes, chopped

parmesan or romano cheese, optional for sprinkling

1. Preheat oven to 190°C.
2. Prepare the Slim Rice as per package instructions (drained and rinsed).
3. Lightly spray peppers with oil, sprinkle salt and bake for 10 mins. Remove to cool.
4. Heat 1 tbsp olive oil in a large pan or skillet over medium heat. Sauté garlic, onions, mushrooms and Italian seasoning until softened (3 mins). Add tomatoes, cook till softened. Add salt and sugar to taste.
5. In a large mixing bowl, combine rice, capers, olives, feta cheese, parsley and half the tomato sauce.
6. Fill the peppers with rice mixture, place them in a baking tray, pour the remaining sauce around peppers. Bake until peppers are lightly brown.
7. Serve with grated parmesan or romano cheese.

WHEAT FREE   GLUTEN FREE

Nutritional Information/Serving

Energy	Protein	Carbo-hydrate	Fat	Saturated Fat	Sodium	Fibre
369 kcal	13.0g	23.0g	22.0g	9.3g	1.4g	12.0g

PORK AND RICE STIR-FRY

1 pack (200g) Slim Rice

250g pork tenderloin, sliced 1/8 inch thick

1 celery, diagonally sliced

1 green pepper, cut into strips

4 spring onions, sliced

4 mushrooms, sliced

1 small tin water-chestnuts, drained

2 tsp ground ginger

170g peas

½ tbsp cornstarch

3 tbsp soy sauce

1 tbsp dry sherry

2 tbsp sunflower oil

1. Prepare the Slim Rice as per package instructions (drained and rinsed).

2. In a large heavy skillet, add oil and stir-fry pork over medium heat, until meat is no longer pink. Add celery, green pepper, onions, mushrooms, water chestnuts and ginger. Stir-fry until vegetables are crisp-tender.

3. Stir in rice and peas, move mixture up the side of skillet, letting the juices cover the bottom of the pan.

4. Mix cornstarch, soy sauce and sherry in a small bowl. Add to juice in pan, cook about 1 min, or until thickened. Toss vegetables and pork with sauce gently to coat.

5. Serve hot and garnish with chives (optional)

Nutritional Information/Serving

Energy	Protein	Carbo-hydrate	Fat	Saturated Fat	Sodium	Fibre
428 kcal	36.0g	14.0g	22.7g	4.8g	1.5g	11.0g

...OOM BARLEY
...TO

Serves	Prep. time	Cook time
2	5 minutes	40 minutes

1 pack (200g) Slim Rice

3 tsp parmesan cheese, grated

1tsp plain flour

2 tbsp full cream

500ml of chicken or veg stock

3 fresh basil, chopped

1 shallot, chopped

150g portabella mushrooms, sliced

100g button mushrooms, sliced

125ml dry white wine

150g pearl barley, sorted and rinsed

1 small onion, chopped

2 tbsp olive oil

1. Prepare the Slim Rice as per package instructions (drained and rinsed).

2. In a saucepan, bring broth to a boil. Cover and turn off heat.

3. Heat 1 tbsp olive oil in a deep skillet. Add onion and sauté until soft. Reduce heat to low. Add barley and rice, and stir. Add wine and cook, stirring, until wine is absorbed. Add flour and full cream and stir.

4. Add hot stock, ½ cup at a time, stirring frequently each time. This should take around 30 minutes.

5. Put remaining oil in a skillet over medium heat and sauté mushrooms and shallots, until golden brown (5 minutes).

6. Stir the mushroom mixture and basil into barley. Season with salt and pepper. Serve and sprinkle with Parmesan cheese.

Nutritional Information/Serving

Energy	Protein	Carbo-hydrate	Fat	Saturated Fat	Sodium	Fibre
367 kcal	19.0g	26.0g	17.3g	10.9g	1.5g	10.0g

The perfect weight loss resource - for everyone

We don't just offer you the most popular low (and sometimes no!) calorie pasta, noodles and rice in the UK and Ireland.

Expert advice, fun and tasty recipes and a vibrant, active (and informative) community - dive into the Slim Hub and join your fellow fitness enthusiasts in sharing favourite recipes, trading information and tips, and everything in between.

Visit us at www.eatwater.co.uk

or get in touch via:

 www.facebook.com/SlimPasta

 www.twitter.com/eat_water

 www.pinterest.com/EatWater

 www.instagram.com/eat_water

 www.youtube.com/EatWaterVideos